Merry go round

You have always thinking of ~~her~~ her
You're in love and you dont know what to say
well I saw her at the fair — she feels
the same way ... she was merry by the merry go round
the merry go round how merrilly we go round
the merry go round

It was the first one of the day
The last one of the night
hold me tight ~~tight~~ hold me tight
They said you were a wrong'un but
I could see in your eyes how your were
gentle & wise & you had the
good stuff ... there's a parade of
girls outside ... that boy's so shy
why'dyou punch out his lights?

heard 'what I like most
about you is your girldfriend
and your shoes' + 'at
half past five we'll swap
agan no but play
that game

(You should not
...
...ray

...on needs every
...an woman & child
She can get her hands
on

7. A...
(Lennon-...
8. THIS BOY
(Lennon-McCartney)
9. CAN'T BUY ME LOVE
...n McCartne...

Babyshambles

This album is dedicated to the loving memory of
Pat's Father, David Walden &
Adam's mother, Lorraine Hutchinson.

Babyshambles are -
Drew McConnell
Patrick Walden
Adam Picek
Peter Doherty

WHAT KATY·DID NEXT

There's this a lesson I have learnt....
if you play with fire, you will get burnt
& hell hath no fury like a woman scorned
I'll tell you my story.... it'll make you wish you'd
you'd never wished you'd never been born

and I may never learn (You never know)
     I may live & learn "..."
     I may crash & burn ...   I may turn to

oh but if you love her tell her you lo...
     you could be kissing her soon
     if you need her tell her you need her
     you won't be missing her soon

think for a love to be true it must come from her how
                                        (a lesson hard learned)

tune in next week for the continuing adventures
of raging Jim.

A'rebors

would you vow today to pay tomorrow
the fuck off big debt (owe to sorrow)

You sent for me
I was knock knock knocking
on death's door
You ignore adore a'rebors
leave the wasted up begging me
if you really cared for me
you let me be set me free
what you rob me of is
my (oh poor me) my liberty
the curtain was calling
or Volair!" (Say Mark) & a'rebors
You were in the mirror
Drawling ....well if you want it
so much go on have it all
if you'd really cared for me
You'd let it be
I'm too polite to say 'fuckoff'
     I say you all you know
ten lines as much as fuck all
that's still nothing at all
what a surprise for us all
a wolfman in spider country
                    down the hall
we've been running round this
world too much girl pretending
not to see what's killing me is
killing you I think I understand that
I misunderstood before your love pla...
me to much more and now I'm free...
I can see again I'm free
But it halt

oh Petty put t
if you've got t
if it's not right
am I oh my oh n
work out a fairer
just paper over the wall
the sun... make you out h
sun.... I just spoke t
the money back.... oh p
do your sums
learn to play no fun
that .... it an undergroun

la la la La
                    underw

In love with a f
well they would if they
if they talk like t
heard a word they
I'm in love with a f
I'm in love with a f
but there's a very odd
I don't mean to a
.... was he su
last for no meaning
                    don't hear
          all I trie

I'm still wai t
fine ... hows yo
book your un tea
Petty gossip
                    hobn

all the time only in a
but they're

Babyshambles: Down in Albion

Artwork by Peter Doherty
Photos by Hedi Slimane
Layout by Jeff Teader & Faber Music Studio

Music arranged by Frank Moon & Alex Davis
Engraved by Camden Music
Edited by Lucy Holliday & Olly Weeks

© 2006 by International Music Publications Ltd
First published by International Music Publications Ltd in 2006
International Music Publications Ltd is a Faber Music company
3 Queen Square, London WC1N 3AU

Printed in England by Caligraving Ltd
All rights reserved

ISBN 0-571-52507-5

To buy Faber Music publications
or to find out about the full range of titles available,
please contact your local music retailer or Faber Music sales enquiries:

Faber Music Ltd, Burnt Mill, Elizabeth Way, Harlow, CM20 2HX England
Tel: +44(0)1279 82 89 82
Fax: +44(0)1279 82 89 83
sales@fabermusic.com fabermusic.com

La Belle et la Bête

Words and Music by Peter Doherty, Robert Chevally and Peter Wolf

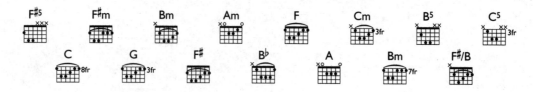

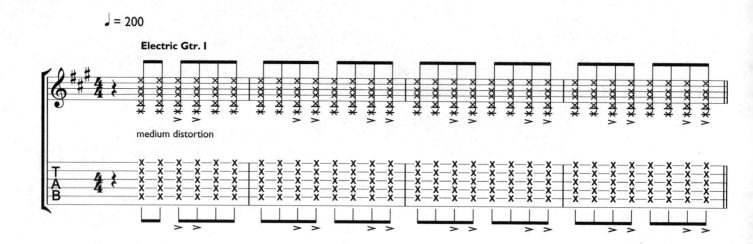

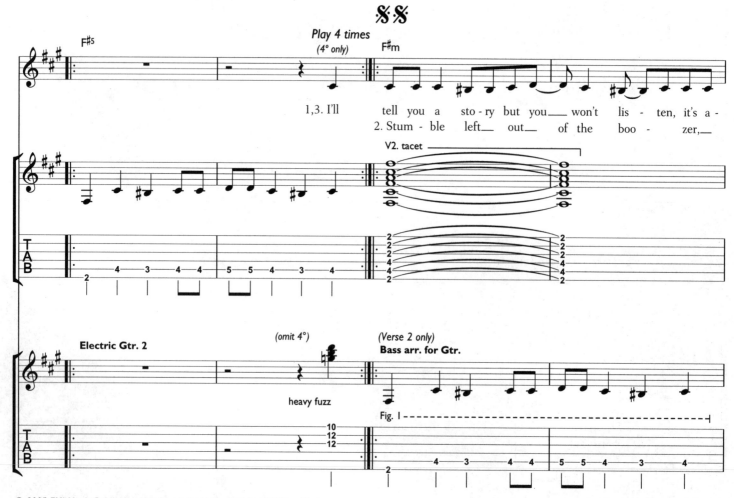

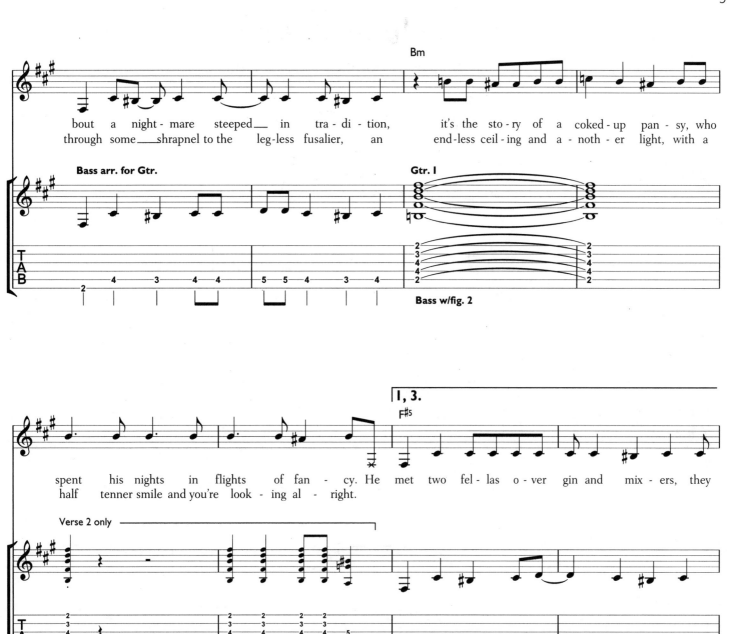

bout a night - mare steeped___ in tra - di - tion,   it's the sto - ry of a coked - up pan - sy, who
through some___ shrapnel to the leg - less fusalier,   an end - less ceil - ing and a - noth - er light, with a

spent his nights in flights of fan - cy. He met two fel - las o - ver gin and mix - ers, they
half tenner smile and you're look - ing al - right.

talked for a while he soon___ got the pic - ture.   One was a souped up So - ho min - cer, and the

On D.%% - much slower and more freely. . . . .

oth - er was a pik - ey with a know-ledge for scrip - tures. Then the con - ver - sa - tion turned

Fig. 2

Bass arr. for Gtr.

Gtr. I

accel.

e - vil, (e - vil), talked and talked and talked a - bout peo - ple:— why did you

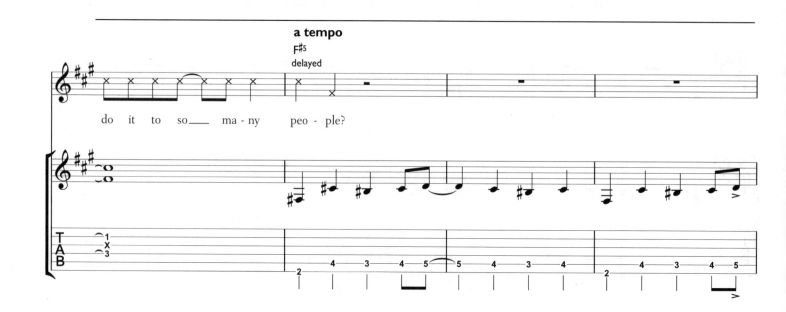

a tempo

F#5

delayed

do it to so__ ma - ny peo - ple?

is she more beau-ti-ful than me?
(she)

She is the belle et la bête of the ball, the

14

Fuck Forever

Words and Music by Peter Doherty and Patrick Walden

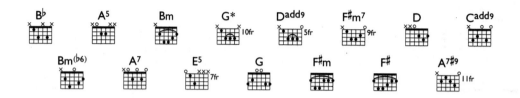

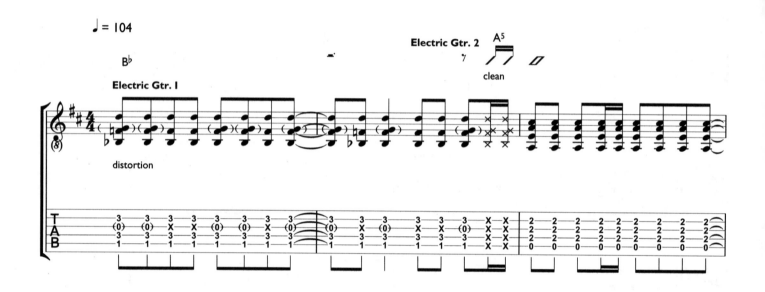

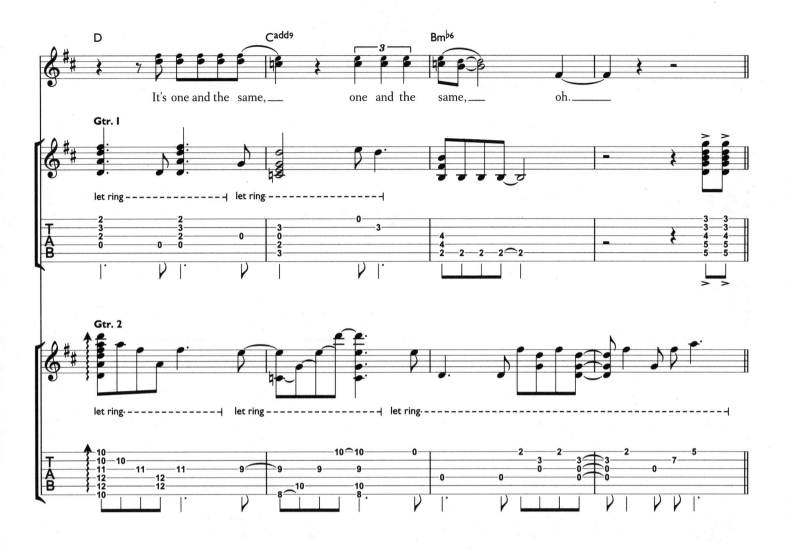

It's one and the same,___ one and the same,___ oh.___

1. So what's the use be-tween death and glo-ry? I can't tell be-tween death and glo-ry.
2. What's the use be-tween death and glo-ry? I can't tell be-tween death and glo-ry,

18

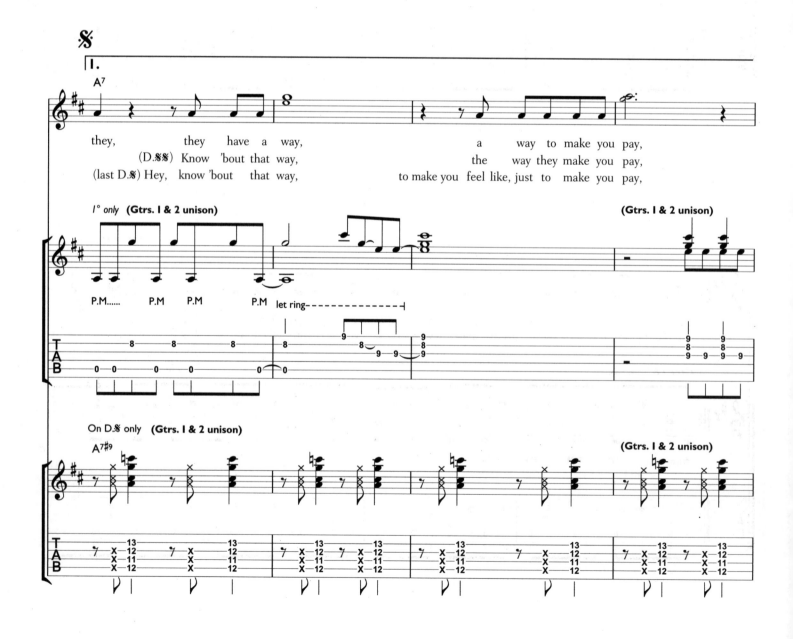

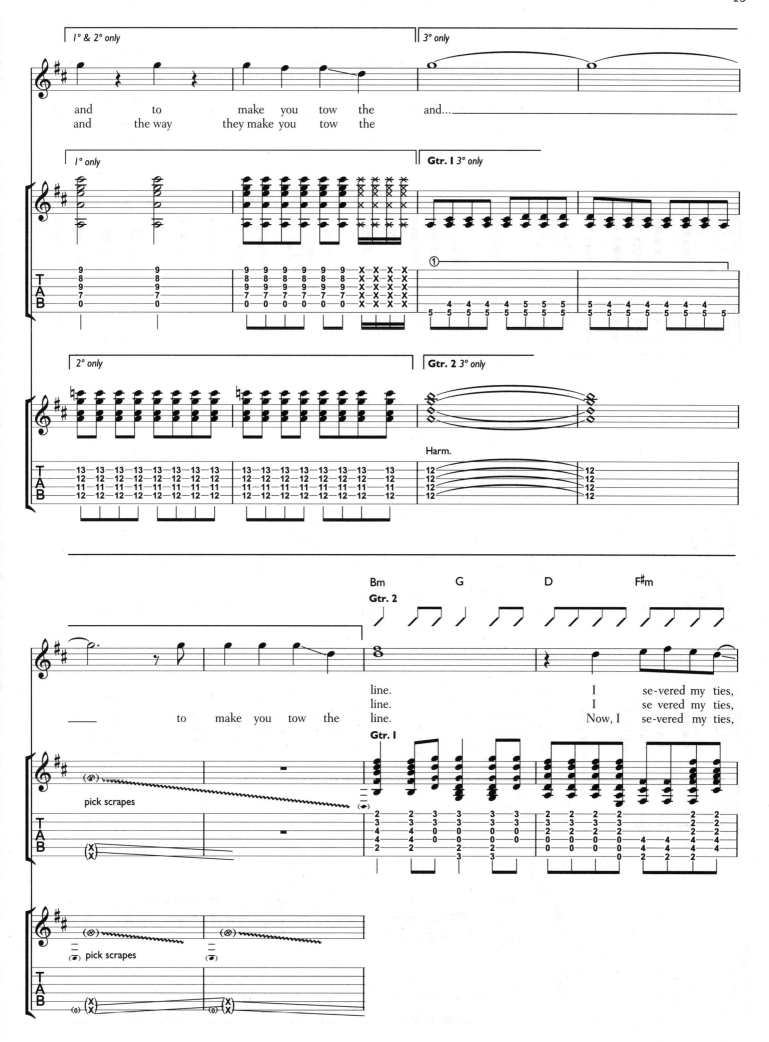

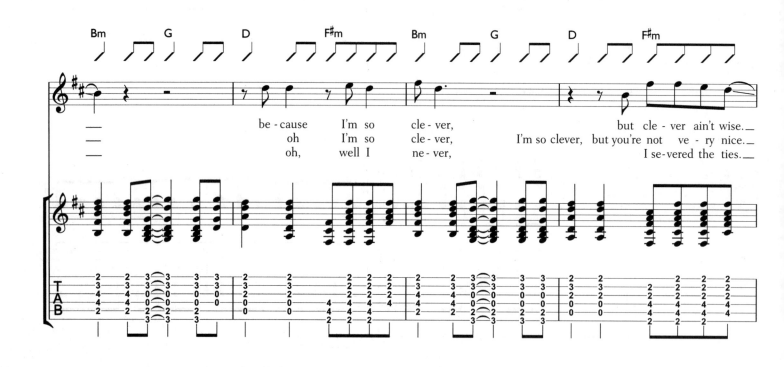

be-cause I'm so cle-ver, but cle-ver ain't wise.
oh I'm so cle-ver, I'm so clever, but you're not ve-ry nice.
oh, well I ne-ver, I se-vered the ties.

And fuck for - e - - ver, if you don't mind,
So fuck for - e - - ver, if you don't mind,
And fuck for - e - - ver, if you don't

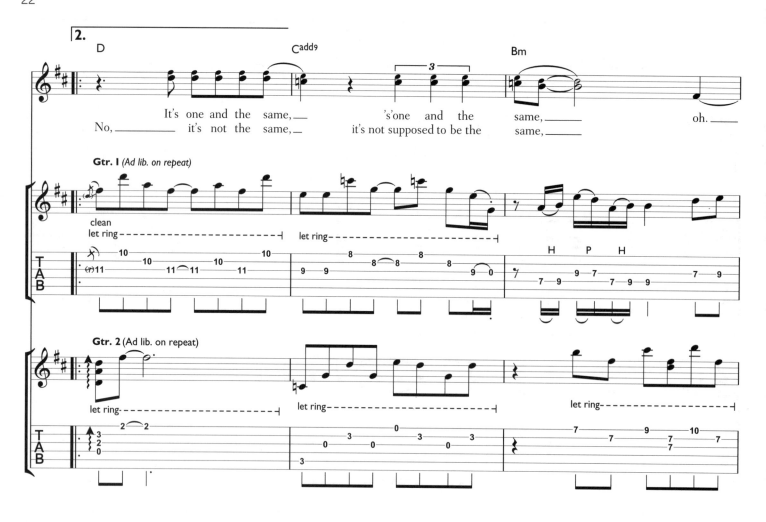

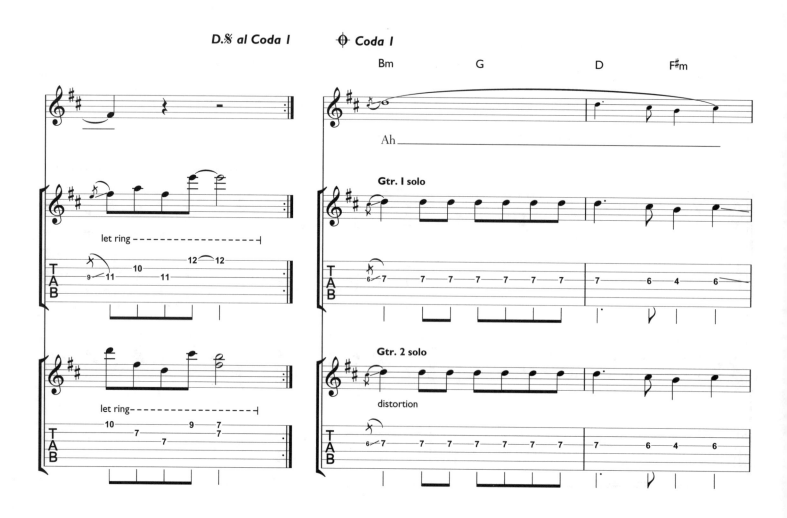

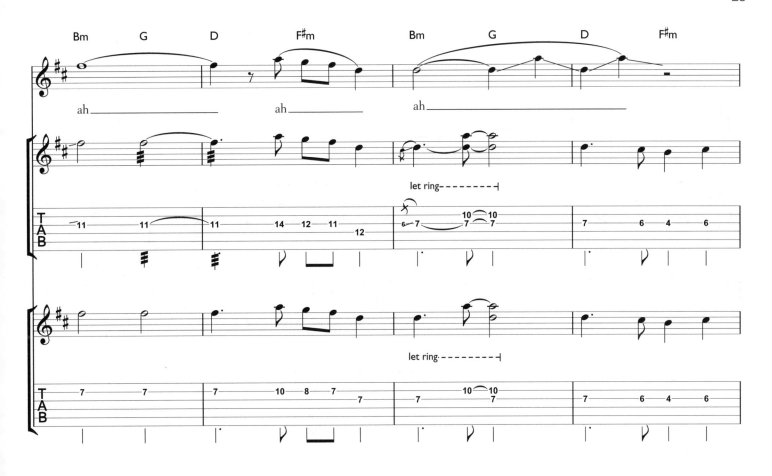

D.% al Coda 2   **Coda 2**

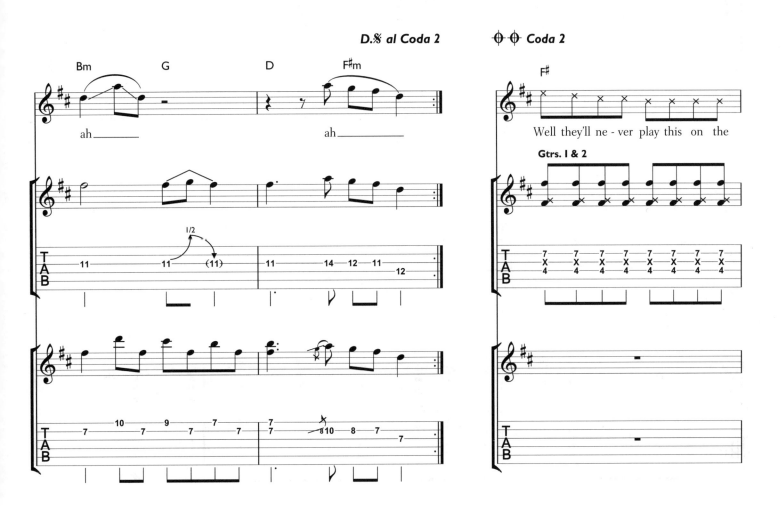

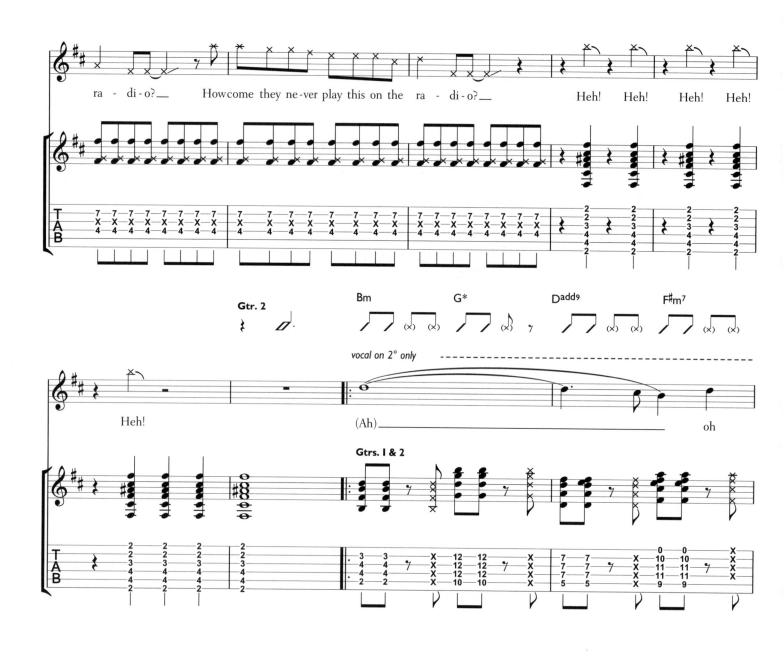

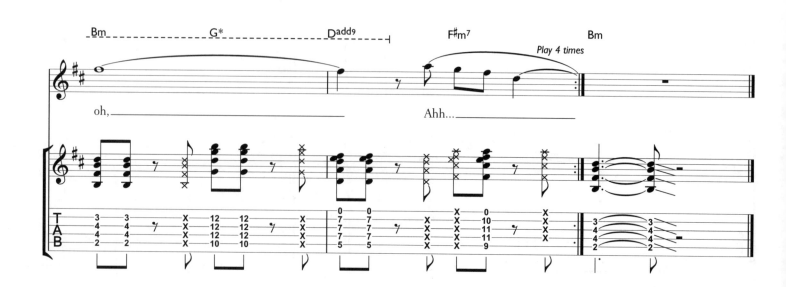

A'rebors

Words and Music by Peter Doherty

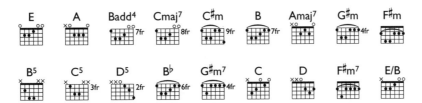

31

The 32nd December

Words and Music by Peter Doherty and Patrick Walden

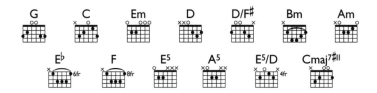

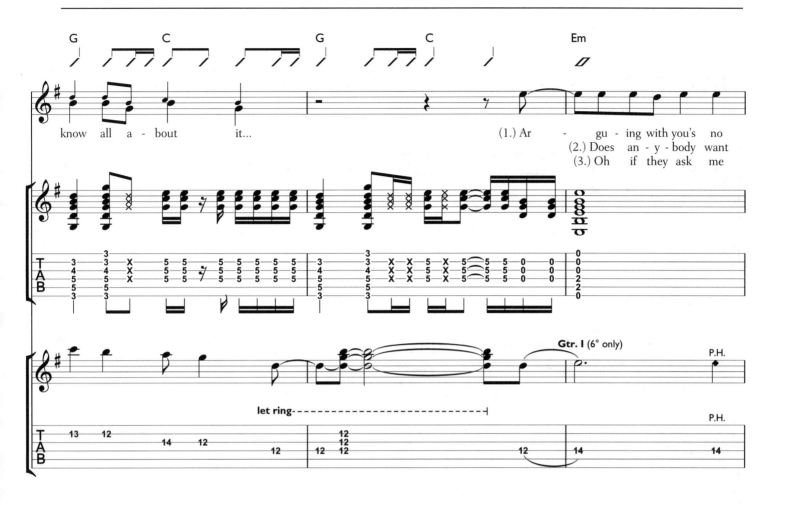

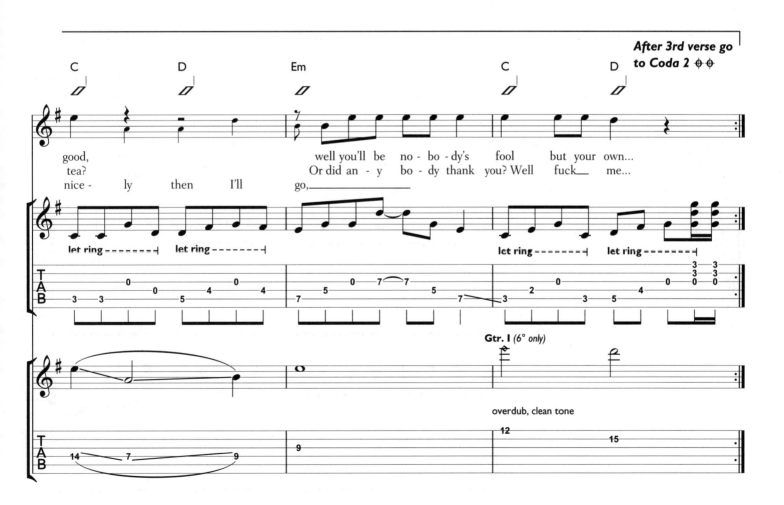

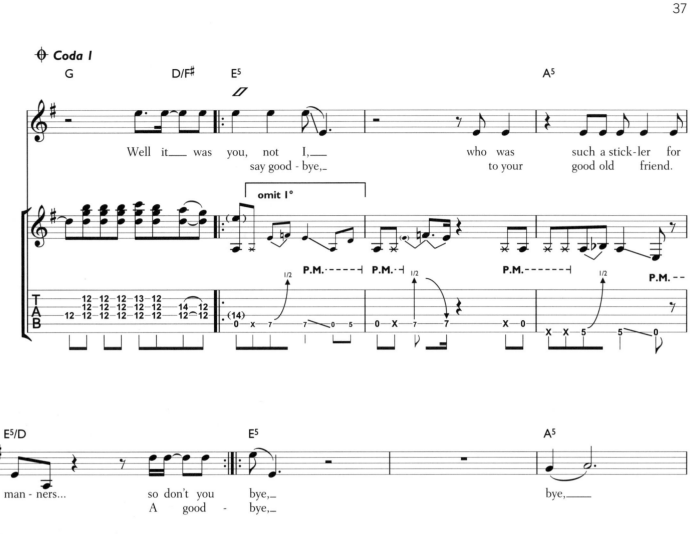

PIPE DOWN

Words and Music by Peter Doherty and Patrick Walden

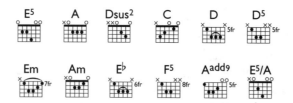

$\quad$ = 130

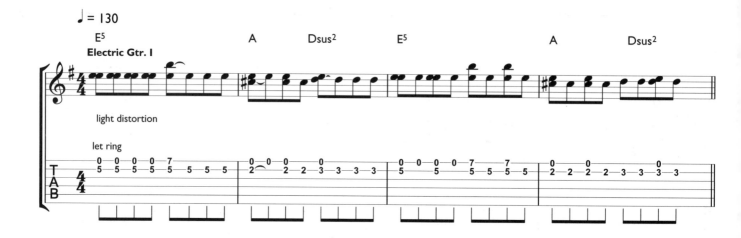

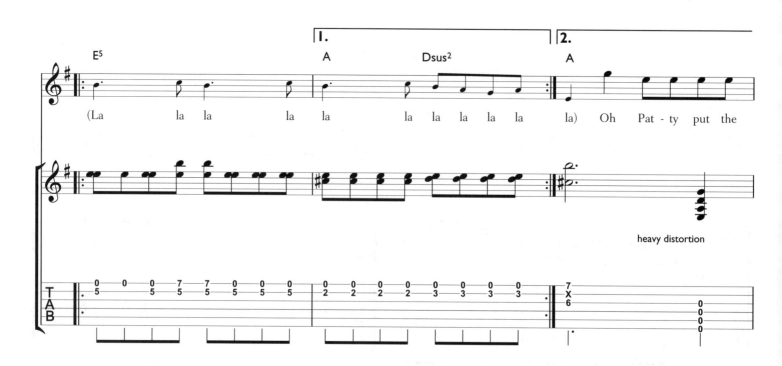

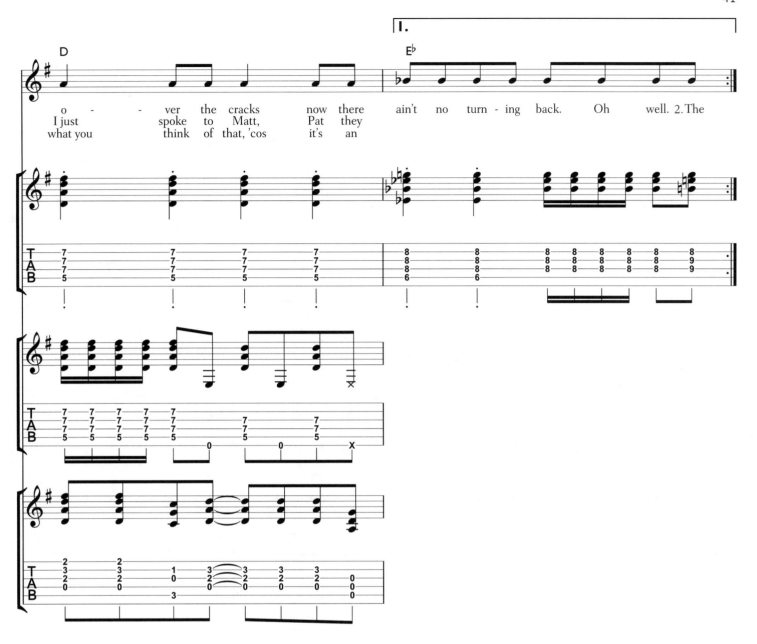

Lyrics (verse 1 / verse 2 lines):
o - - ver the cracks now there ain't no turn - ing back. Oh well. 2. The
I just spoke to Matt, Pat they think of that, 'cos it's an

D.%% & take 3rd time bar

D.%% al Coda I

Lyrics:
2. want the mon - ey back. Oh put the **3.** un - der - group trap. You'd bet - ter

(Gtr. I verse 2 only)

(Gtr. I verse 3 only)

42

Sticks and Stones

Words and Music by Peter Doherty and Peter Wolfe

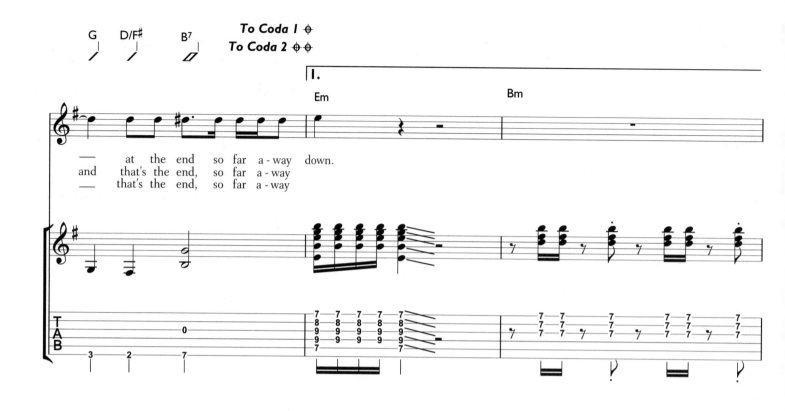

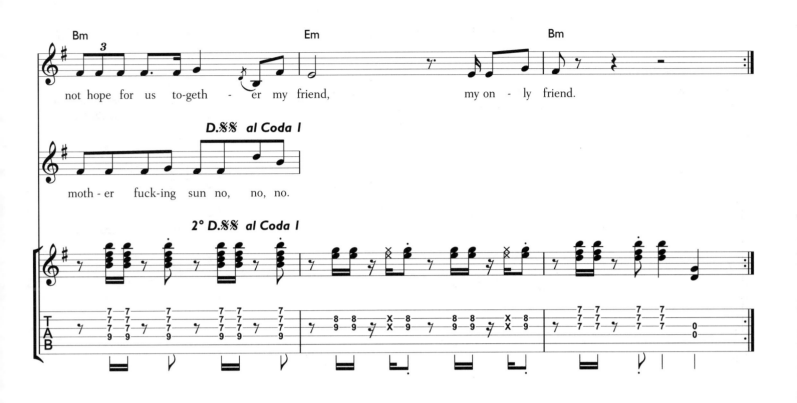

not hope for us to-geth - er my friend, my on - ly friend.

D.%% al Coda I

moth - er fuck-ing sun no, no, no.

2° D.%% al Coda I

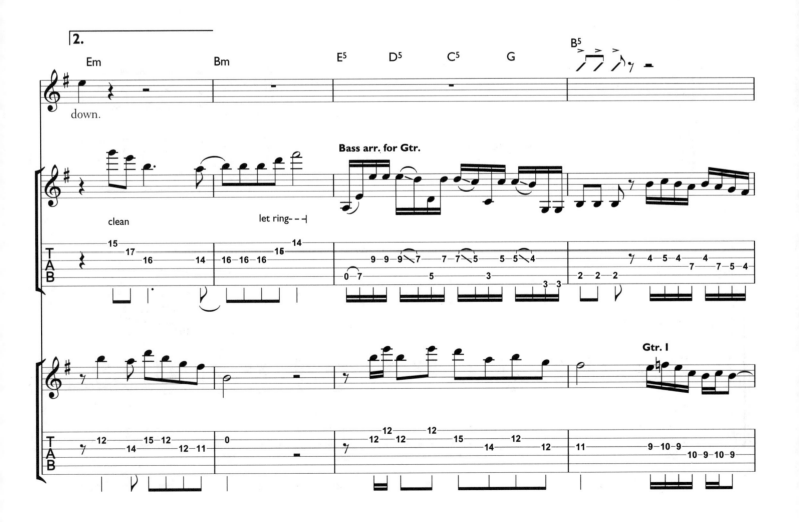

2.

down.

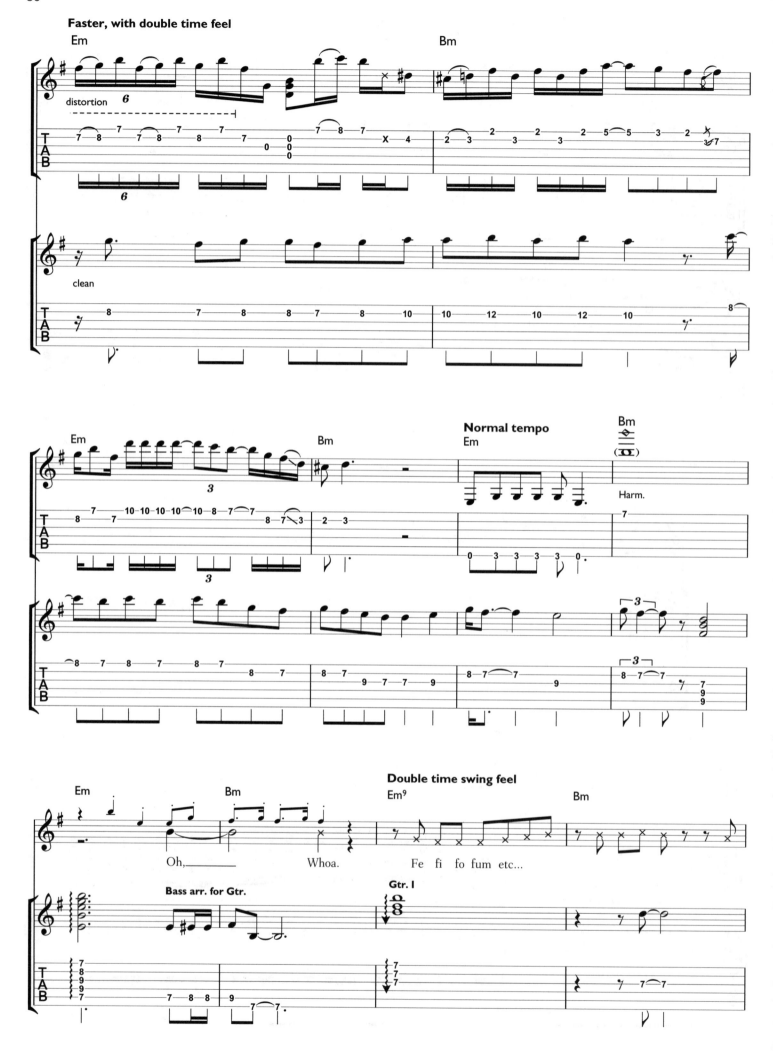

KILLAMANGIRO

Words and Music by Peter Doherty

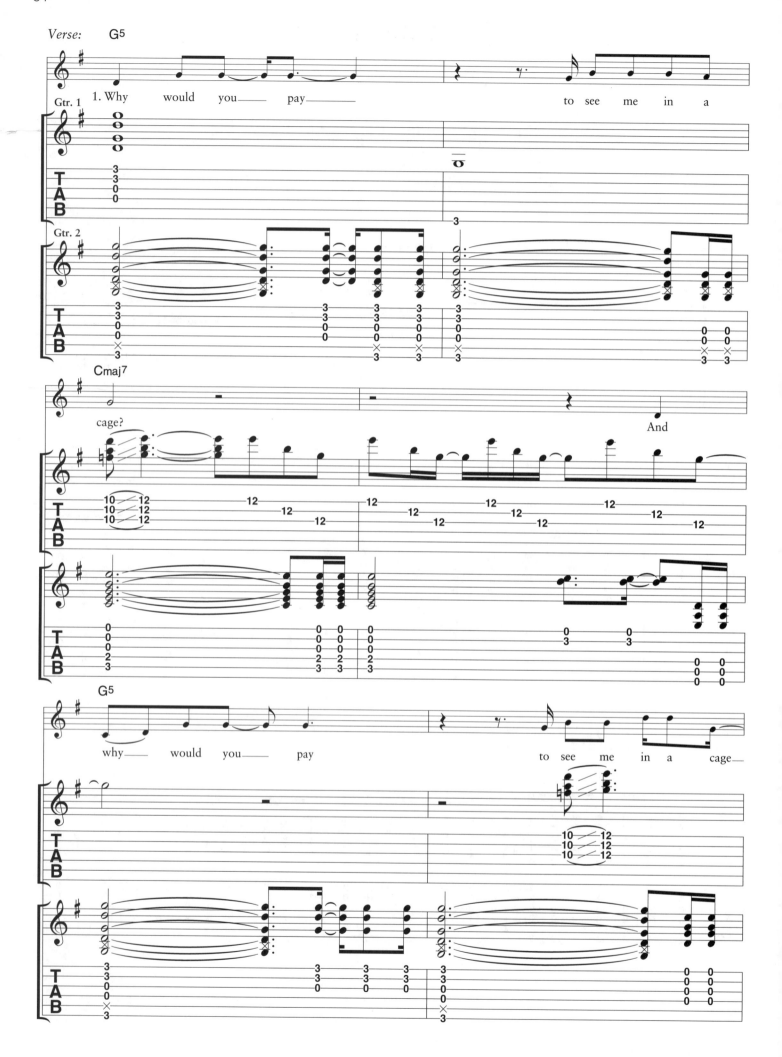

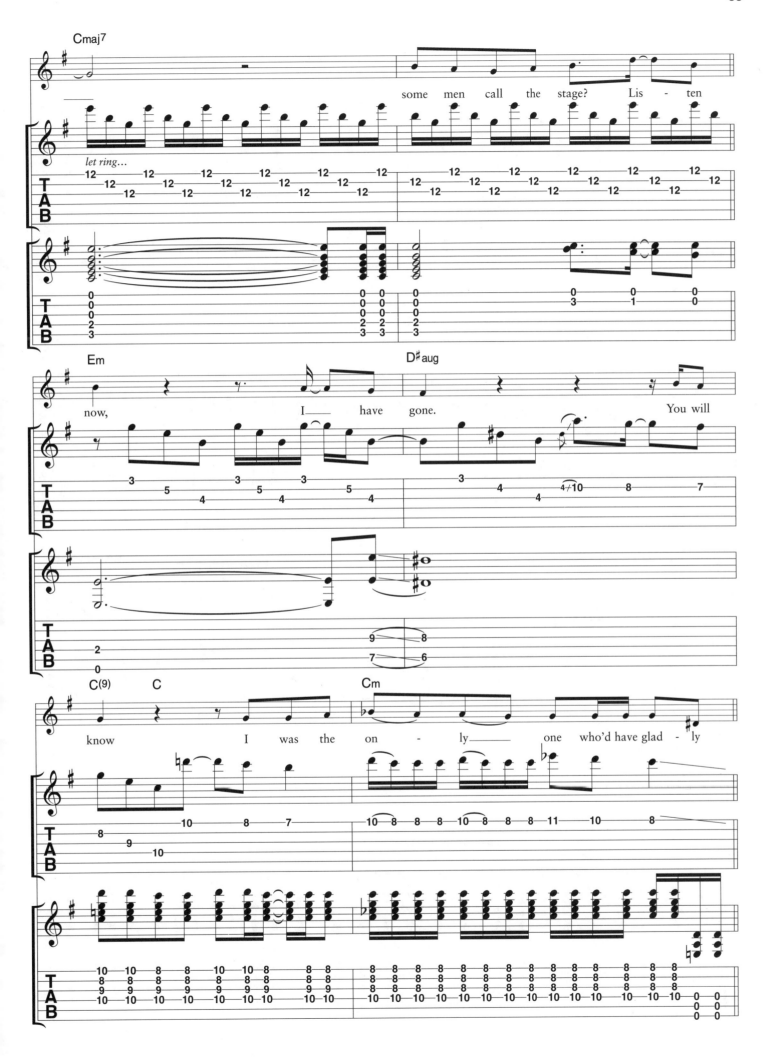

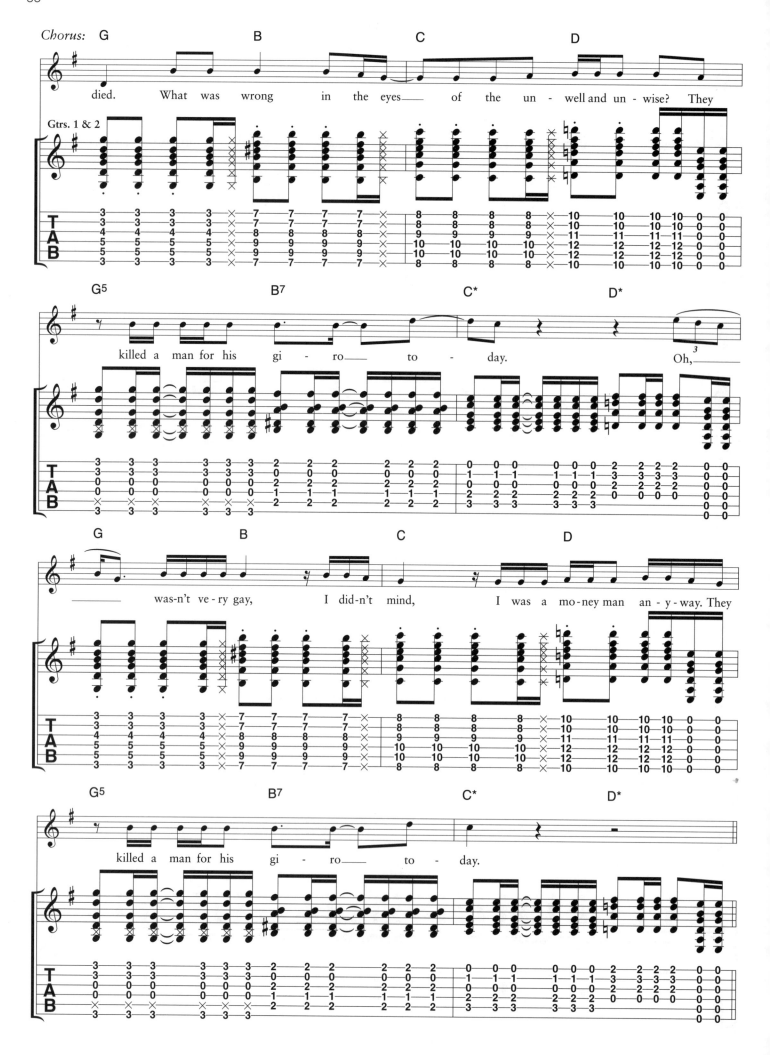

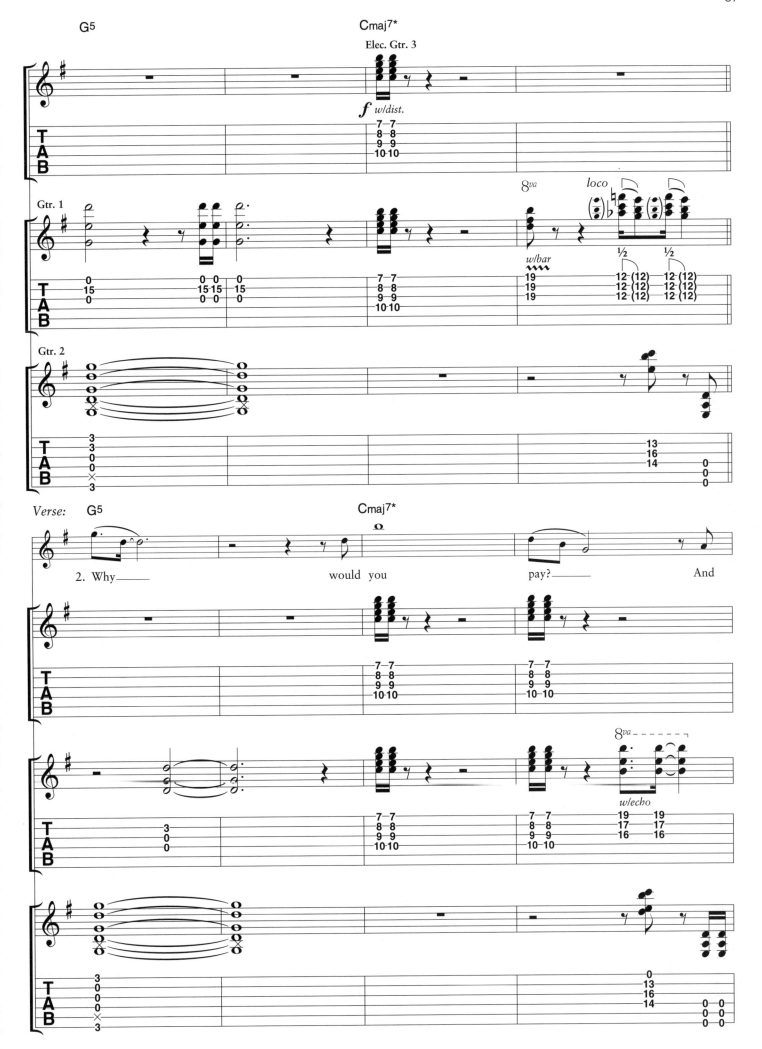

58

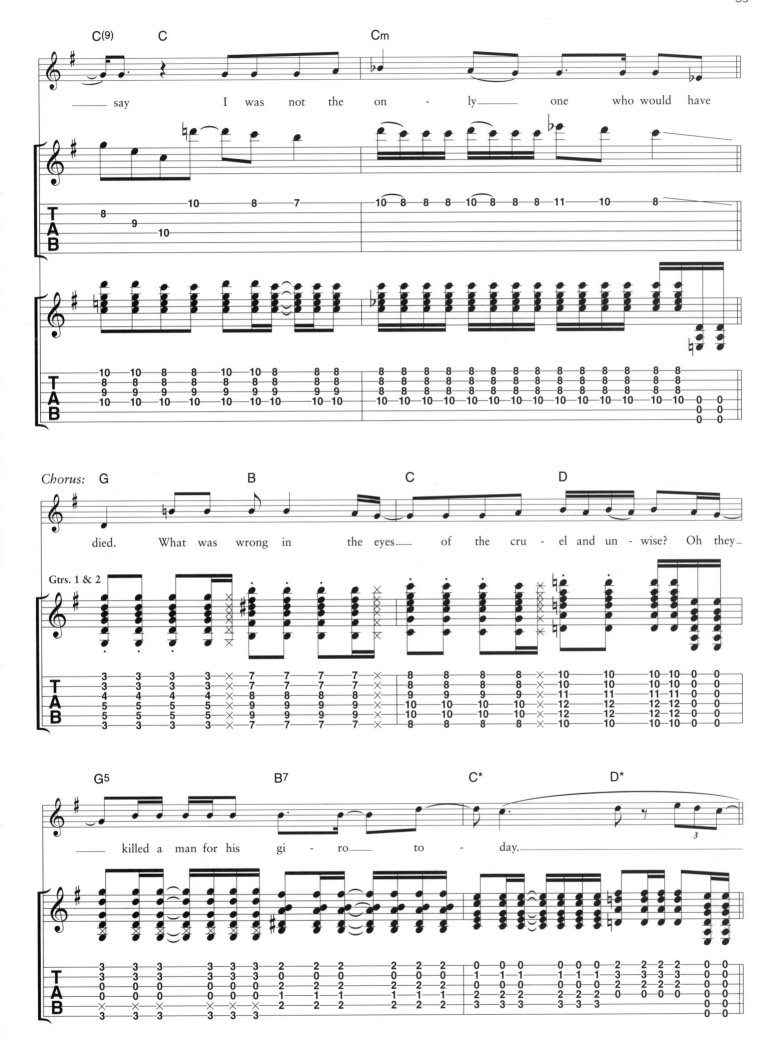

60

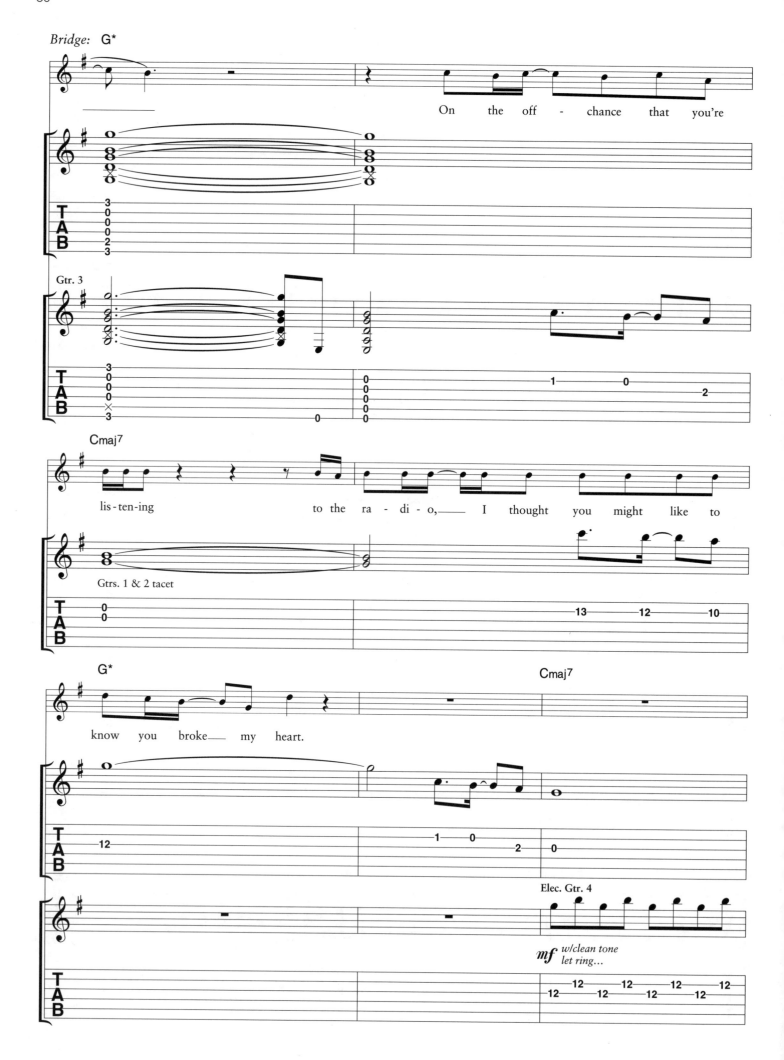

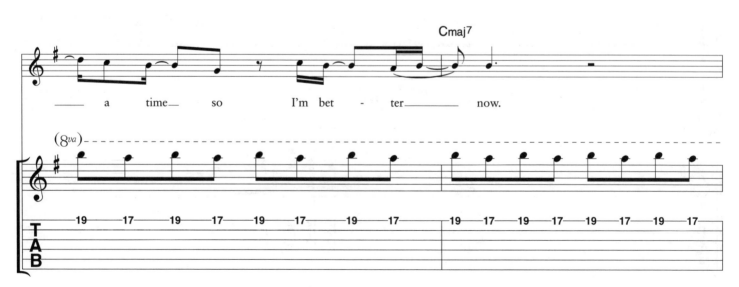

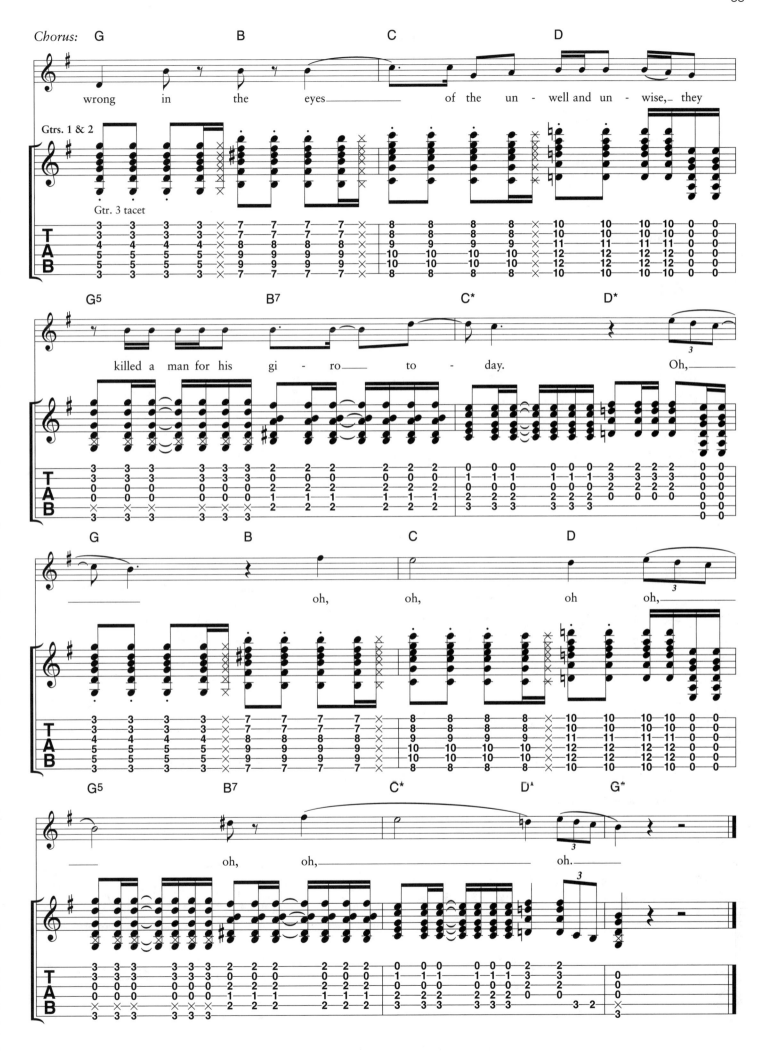

8 Dead Boys

Words and Music by Peter Doherty and Patrick Walden

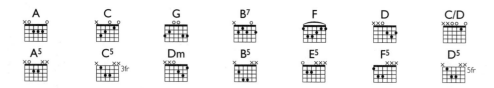

68

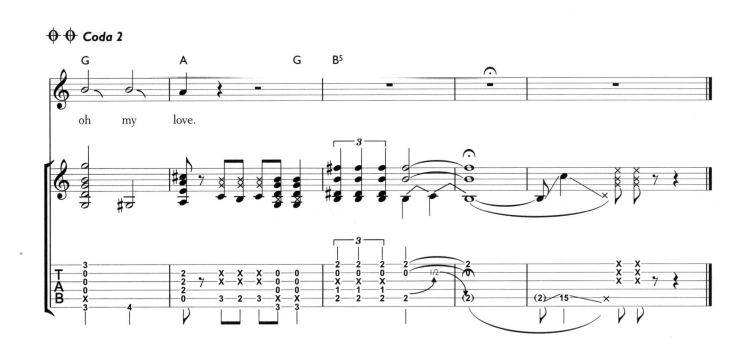

F G Dm
want-ed was not in store, be in the
D.𝄋𝄋𝄋 (with repeat)
al Coda 2
F G
dark once a - gain.
Coda 2
G A G B5
oh my love.

In Love With A Feeling

Words and Music by Peter Doherty and Patrick Walden

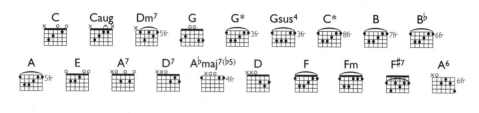

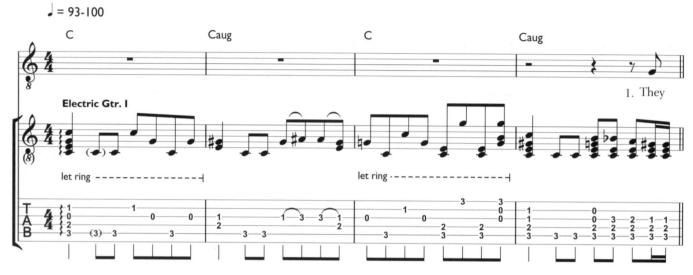

Pentonville

Words and Music by Peter Doherty and General Santana

flatten 1st finger & randomly
slide down whilst striking strings

All the same, who get re - tain, some man jump out_ of their brains. True they
we, Dem dere youth, Jah Jah know dem have fe free we. Here's Ca - lu - ka,_ and Bou - ti - li-
Indian, China - man down from Vi - et - nam, and whole heap of peo - ple from the Ca - rib - be - an.__

can't take the pres - sure, can't take the pain, when they see their life it gone down the drain.
- ro, dem dere youth are some real Ras - ta li - ro. Dem there youth yah couldn't draw ze -
Eng - lish, Scot - tish and Ir - ish man, come to ge - ther and sing this a one.

2° To Coda 1 ⊕
3° D.𝄋𝄋
4° To Coda 2 ⊕ ⊕

boom down the mic__ black and white, In the Pen - ton - ville it is a diff - erent ball game, it's
- ro. Ca' dem a Ras - ta a ze - ro be - cause it
Man,_ to sur - vive this then we have to un - ite.

Dem there youth man, they could-n't hold__ me, me said dem know they have to free we, yo.

(Pete:) No, no

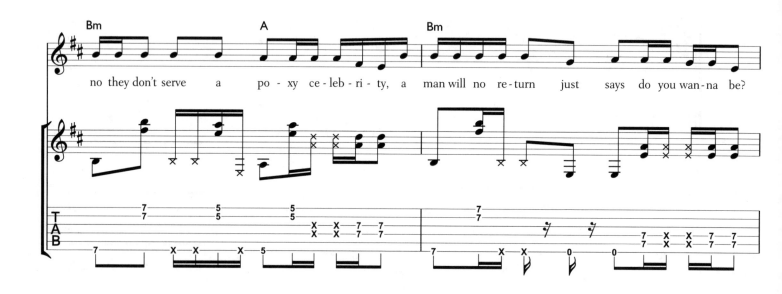

no they don't serve a po - xy ce - leb - ri - ty, a man will no re - turn just says do you wan-na be?

D.𝄋𝄋 al § twice

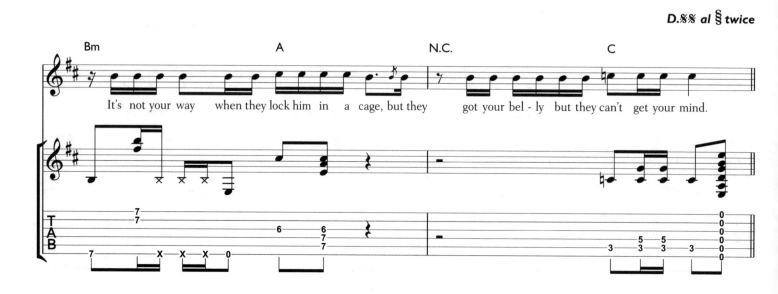

It's not your way when they lock him in a cage, but they got your bel - ly but they can't get your mind.

What Katy Did Next

Words and Music by Peter Doherty and Alan Wass

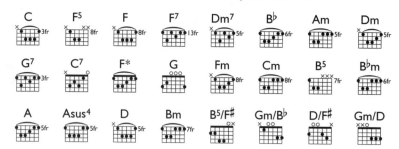

88

Albion

Words and Music by Peter Doherty

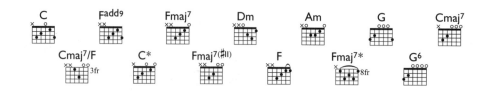

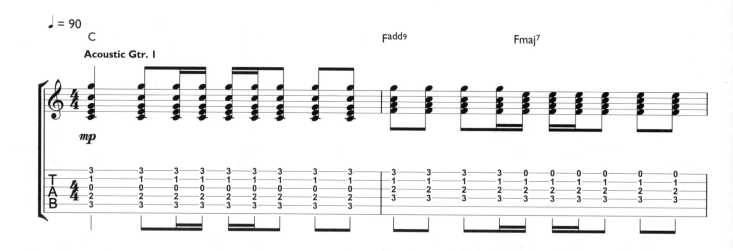

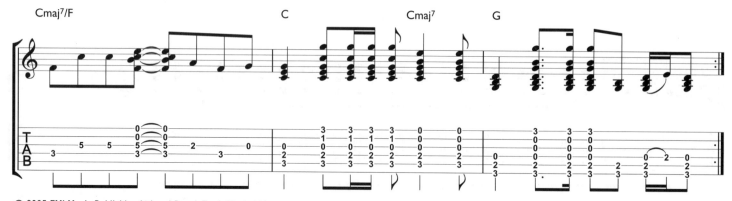

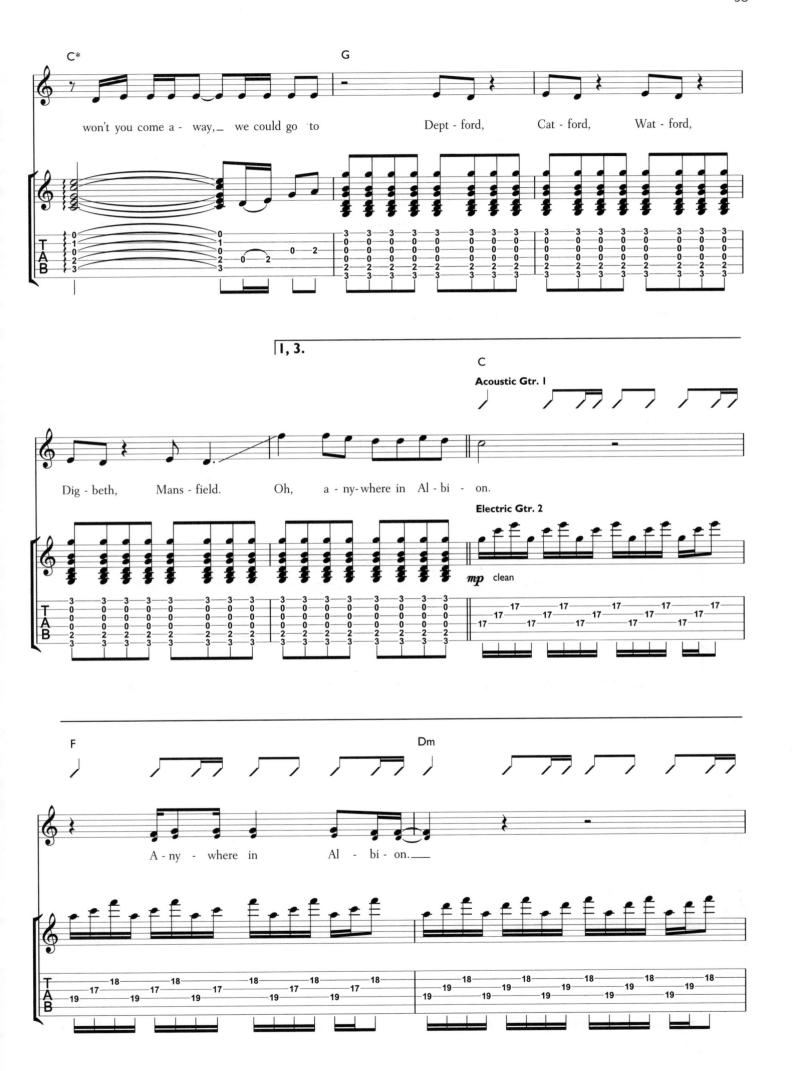

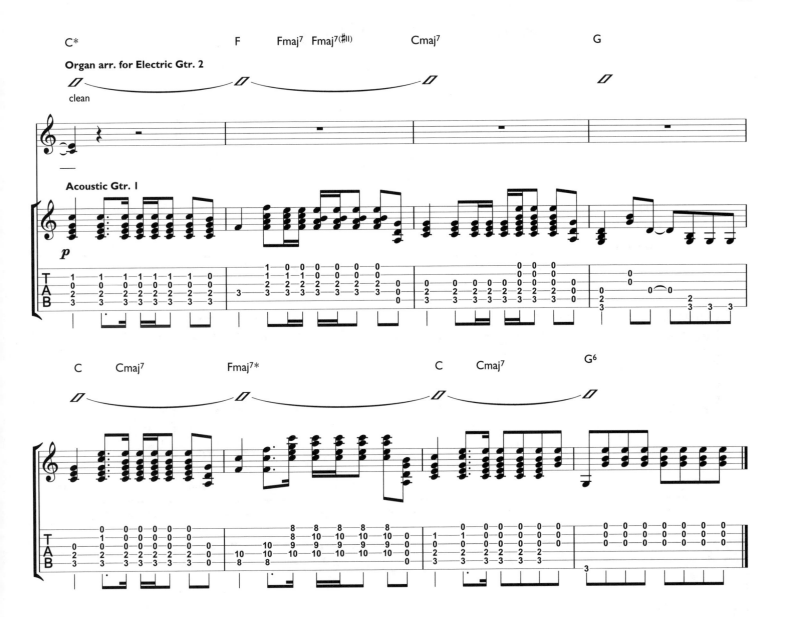

Chorus 2:
If you're looking for a cheap sort all glint with perspiration
There's a four mile queue outside the disused power station
Now come away, oh say you'll come away, go to
Satsworth, Senworth, Weovil, Woomoyle, Newcastle

Chorus 3:
And if you are looking for a cheap tart, don't glint with perspiration
There's a five mile queue outside the disused power station
Now come away, won't you come away, we'll go to
Bedtown, Oldham, Nunthorpe, Rowlan, Bristol
Anywhere in Albion.

Back From The Dead

Words and Music by Peter Doherty, Carl Barat, Peter Wolfe and Matt White

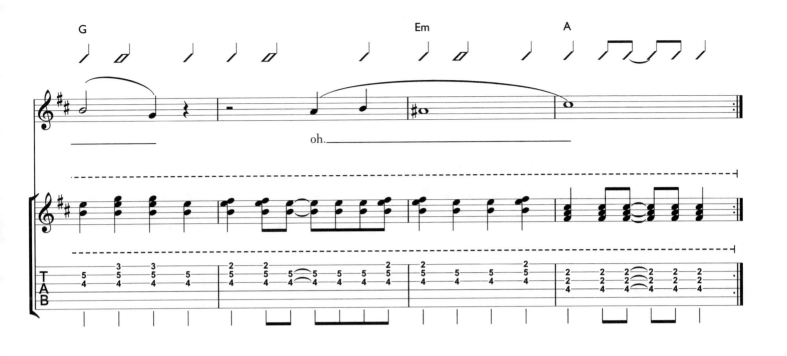

1. I heard it said you had come back from the dead, and you were

Refer to block lyric for all verses

Backing Vox sing Fig. 1

Electric Gtr. 1

clean

Electric Guitar plays Fig. 1

1° (Vs. 1) Repeat section x 5
2° (Vs. 2) Repeat section x 4 till ⊕

To Coda ⊕

play - ing so fine, scoo - ping up the soul of the wine

Electric Gtr. 2

clean

cor - ner.

Bass arr. for Electric Gtr. 1

clean

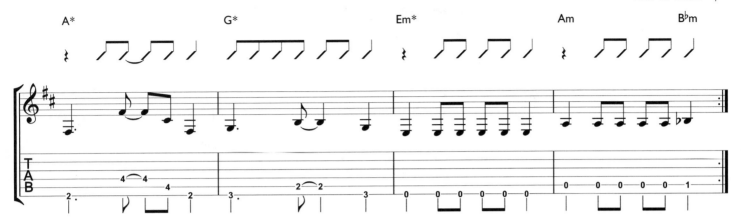

✛ *Coda*   Music slows right down - played freely from this point

Verse 1:
I heard it said you had come back from the dead
And you were playing so fine, scooping up the soul of the wine
Encourage my boy away, look them in the eye
Try not to look too scully, if you want some money and you need someone.
And now oh this ain't no happy place to be
There's nothing nice around me, nothing nice about me, almost everyone agrees
It's a hell of a year for you, and me my friend
Oh promises, promises, I know you've heard them all before
Love is, love is, love is, love is
Love is, oh well it's just around the corner.

Verse 2:
I heard it said you had come back from the dead
Playing so fine, even if you were short on time
Oh, encourage my boy away, look them in the eye
Like they try to be funny if you need someone...

Loyalty Song

Words and Music by Peter Doherty and Patrick Walden

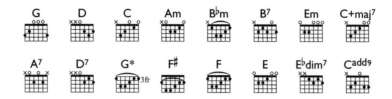

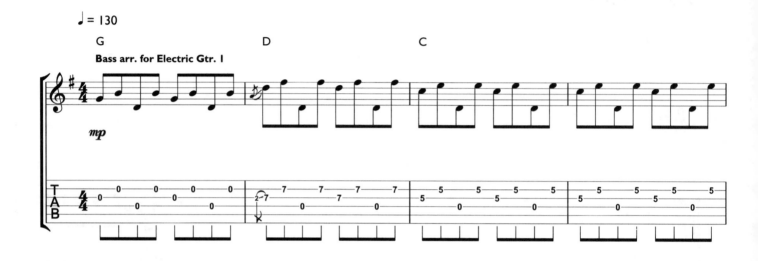

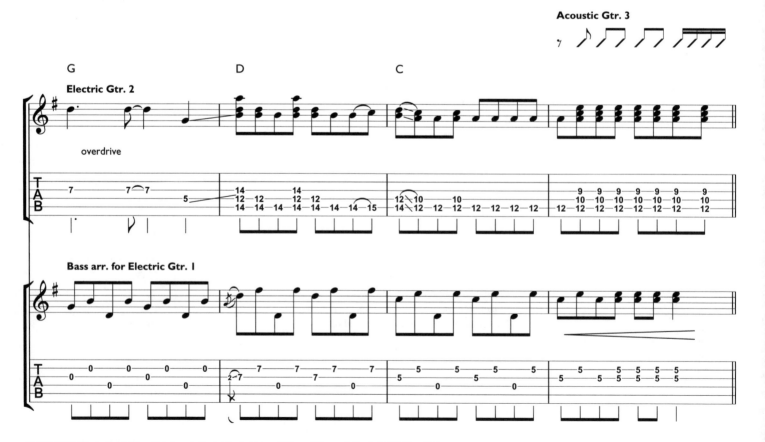

102

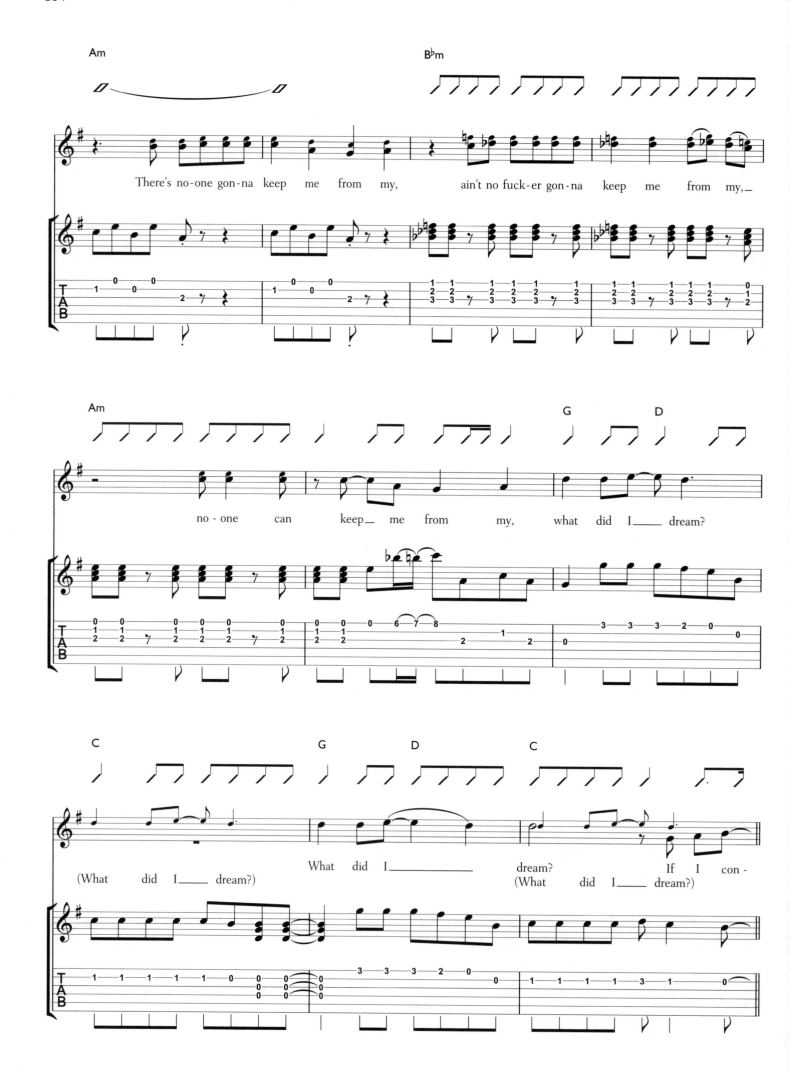

slight crack in my chi - m - ney.

Oh tell me

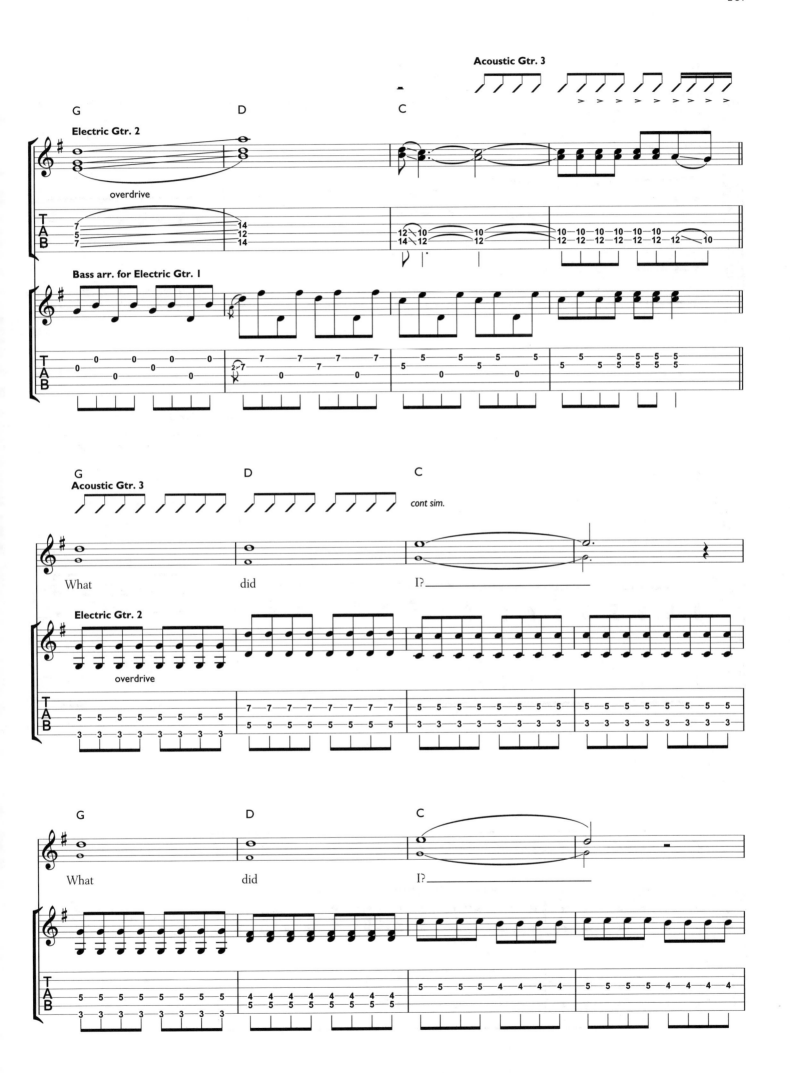

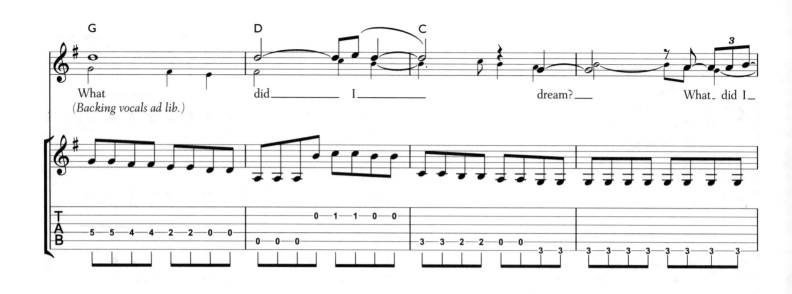

What did I dream? What did I
(Backing vocals ad lib.)

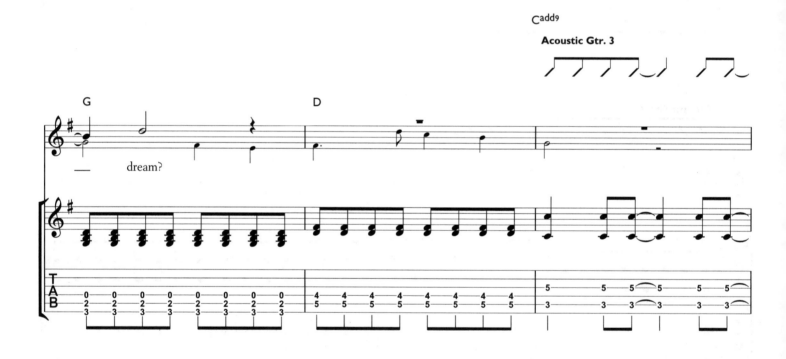

dream?

Acoustic Gtr. 3

Cadd9

rall.

Up The Morning

Words and Music by Peter Doherty and Patrick Walden

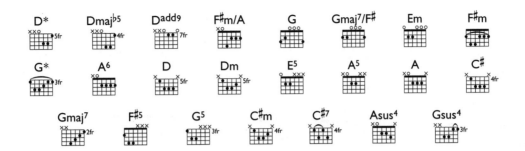

111

But ev - 'ry - time I see your face, makes me cry,_____ al - ways.___

Piano arr. for Gtr.

Gtr.

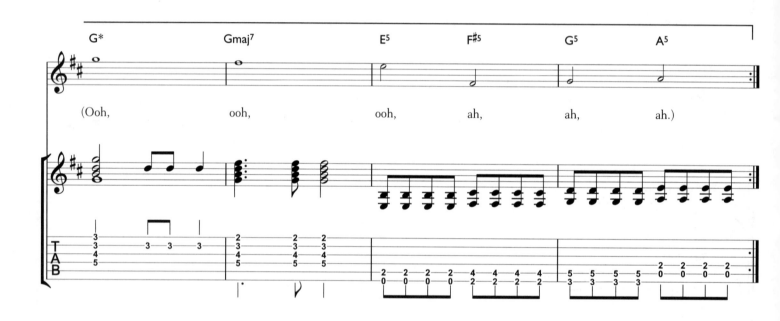

(Ooh, ooh, ooh, ah, ah, ah.)

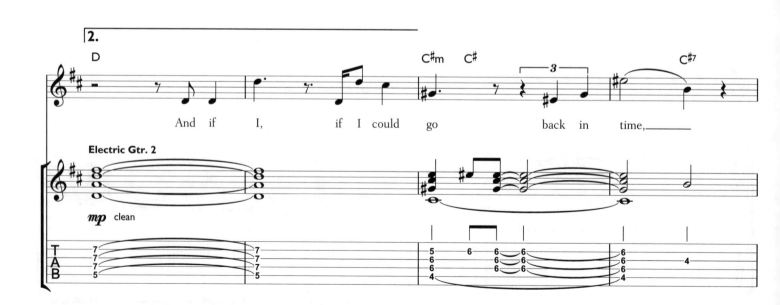

2.

And if I, if I could go back in time,_____

Electric Gtr. 2

mp clean

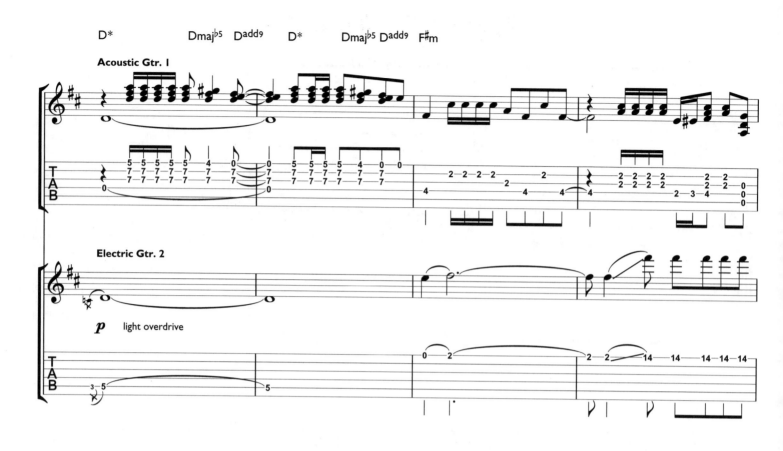

Merry Go Round

Words and Music by Peter Doherty

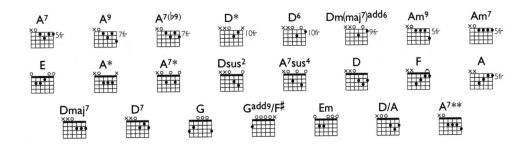

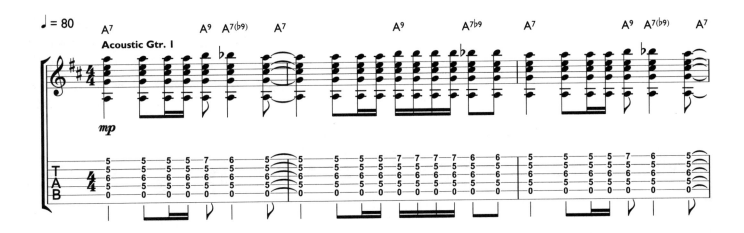

You have al - ways, think - ing of her.
The mer - ry go round. ____

118

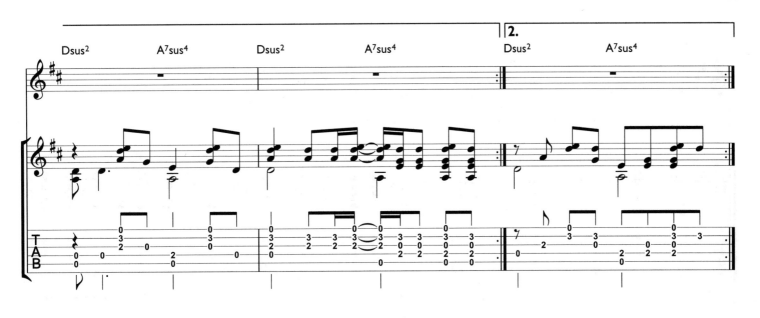

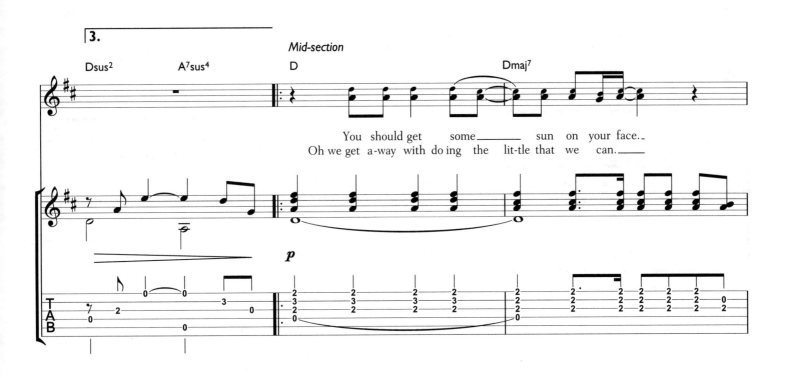

Mid-section

You should get some_____ sun on your face._
Oh we get a-way with do-ing the lit-tle that we can.____

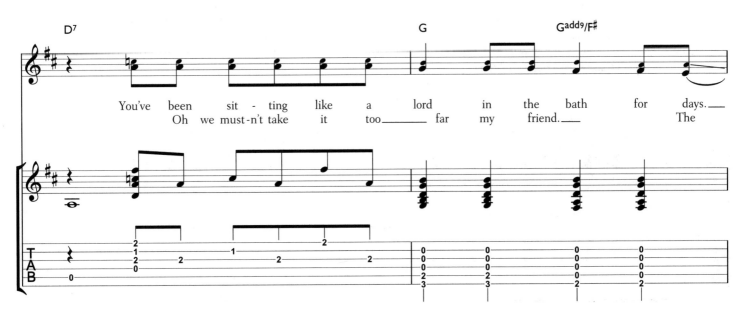

You've been sit-ting like a lord in the bath for days._
Oh we must-n't take it too_____ far my friend.____ The

122

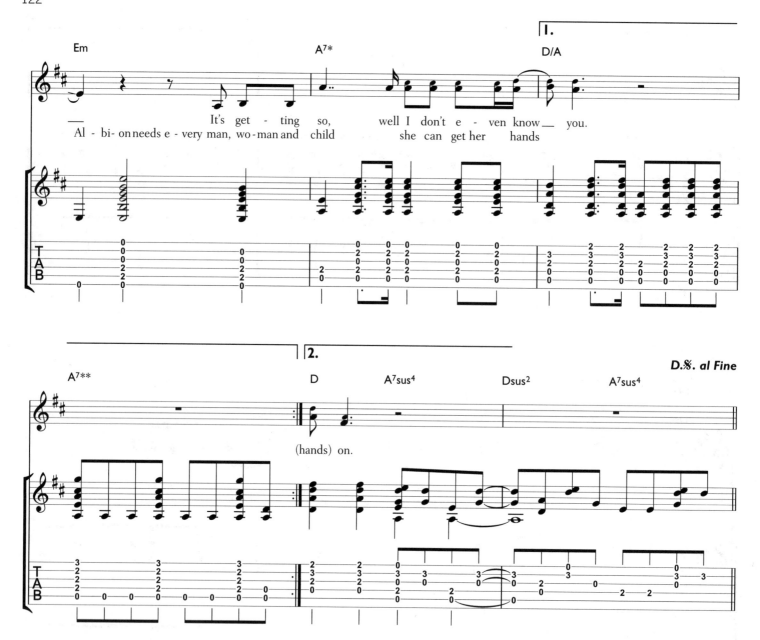

Verse 3:

It was the first one of the day
It was the last one of the night
Oh mop it up, she'll be alright
Mop it up, she'll be alright
There's a parade and all outside
Come on and feel the air outside...

Verse 4:

Said what I like most about you, Pete
Is your girlfriend and your shoes
And you think, well half past five, we'll swap again
Half past five we'll swap again
Oh there's a parade of girls outside
The boy's so shy
Why d'you punch out his lights?

Verse 5:

It was the first one of the day
It was the last one of the night
Oh hold me tight, hold me tight, hold me tight yeah.
They said you were a wrong'un
But I could see in your eyes
How you were gentle and wise
And you had the good stuff
And there's a parade of girls outside
I've been so good to that boy
Why did he steal all my lighters?